The Monster Cook Book

St Georges C of E Foundation
School Primary Phase
Westwood Road
Broadstairs

PHASE 5

/ou/
ea/i_e/

Level 6 – Orange

BookLife
Readers

Helpful Hints for Reading at Home

The graphemes (written letters) and phonemes (units of sound) used throughout this series are aligned with Letters and Sounds. This offers a consistent approach to learning whether reading at home or in the classroom.

HERE IS A LIST OF PHONEMES FOR THIS PHASE OF LEARNING. AN EXAMPLE OF THE PRONUNCIATION CAN BE FOUND IN BRACKETS.

Phase 5			
ay (day)	ou (out)	ie (tie)	ea (eat)
oy (boy)	ir (girl)	ue (blue)	aw (saw)
wh (when)	ph (photo)	ew (new)	oe (toe)
au (Paul)	a_e (make)	e_e (these)	i_e (like)
o_e (home)	u_e(rule)		

Phase 5 Alternative Pronunciations of Graphemes			
a (hat, what)	e (bed, she)	i (fin, find)	o (hot, so, other)
u (but, unit)	c (cat, cent)	g (got, giant)	ow (cow, blow)
ie (tied, field)	ea (eat, bread)	er (farmer, herb)	ch (chin, school, chef)
y (yes, by, very)	ou (out, shoulder, could, you)		

HERE ARE SOME WORDS WHICH YOUR CHILD MAY FIND TRICKY.

Phase 5 Tricky Words			
oh	their	people	Mr
Mrs	looked	called	asked
could			

TOP TIPS FOR HELPING YOUR CHILD TO READ:

- Allow children time to break down unfamiliar words into units of sound and then encourage children to string these sounds together to create the word.

- Encourage your child to point out any focus phonics when they are used.

- Read through the book more than once to grow confidence.

- Ask simple questions about the text to assess understanding.

- Encourage children to use illustrations as prompts.

PHASE 5
/ou/
ea/i_e/

This book focuses on the phonemes /ou/ /ea/ and /i_e/ and is an orange level 6 book band.

The Monster Cook Book

Written by
Shalini Vallepur

Illustrated by
Drue Rintoul

The monsters from the Moon were going down to Earth for a visit. Blinks, Jam and Zozo were eager to visit the monsters on Earth.

But they could not go down to Earth without something! "We have to go to Earth with a big gift," said Jam.

"What should we bring?" Blinks asked.
"I know! We can cook a big dinner for the monsters on Earth," said Zozo.

"That is a top plan. We can use The Monster Cook Book. It has lots of cool food for all sorts of monsters," said Jam.

The three monsters rushed to the bookshelf to get The Monster Cook Book.

They took out The Monster Cook Book.
It was big and pink with a long soft tail.
"Let us look and see if we can see something
to cook!" Zozo said.

THE
MONSTER
COOK-
BOOK

"Some monsters are big and frightening," said Jam, reading from the cook book.

"Big monsters eat food that crunches. They eat sandwiches that have things that crunch inside them," said Jam.

"Some monsters are small and they have small lunchboxes," said Blinks.
"What can we cook that is small?" asked Jam.

Looking in The Monster Cook Book, Zozo said, "We can cook small rotting cupcakes for small monsters. But they do need to smell!"

"There are lots of monsters with three eyes. They like to eat all sorts of things. But they love drinking things the most," said Blinks.

"They like smoothies the best. The smoothie has to smell like fish that has gone off," said Jam after reading the book.

"There are so many different monsters on Earth!" said Zozo.
"We'd better start cooking a big dinner for all the monsters," said Jam.

The three monsters from the Moon started to cook. They made all sorts of disgusting foods that crunched and smelt for the monsters on Earth.

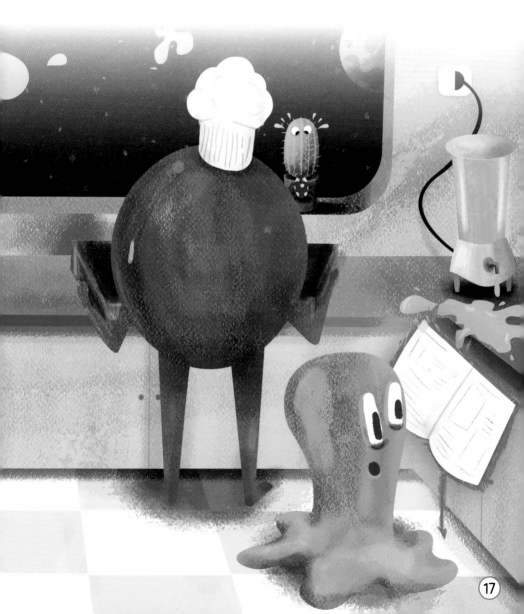

Soon, they had lots of food to bring down
to Earth.

"To the rocket on the roof!" Zozo yelled.
They rushed to the big rocket that was parked
on the roof. All the food was packed in a big
lunchbox.

BOOM! With a big bang, the rocket took off!
It zoomed down to Earth.

Blinks, Jam and Zozo shot past bright stars. It was amazing! The light from the Sun filled the rocket.

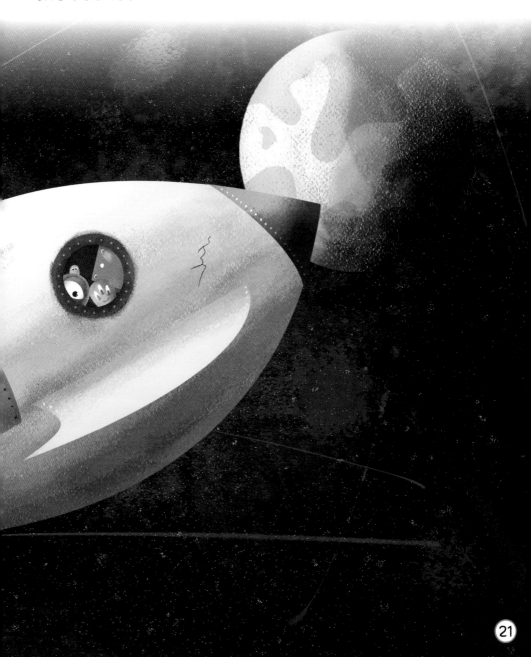

Soon, they landed on Earth for their visit.
They took the big lunchbox off the rocket.

"Hello monsters of Earth! We are the monsters from the Moon!" Jam said to all the monsters in the park.

"We have lots of food for you! Sandwiches to crunch for the big monsters, small cupcakes for small monsters and smoothies that stink for the three-eyed monsters," said Jam.

"Thank you!" said the monsters from Earth.
They began to eat food from the lunchbox.

But something was not right. The big monsters took the small cupcakes, and the small monsters drank the smoothies that stank. The three-eyed monsters munched all of the sandwiches that crunched!

"Stop!" yelled Jam. "We followed The Monster Cook Book, but no one is eating the correct thing?"

"The Monster Cook Book is right, but we monsters can eat anything that we want," said an Earth monster with a grunt. "I don't have to eat sandwiches that crunch all the time just because I am big."

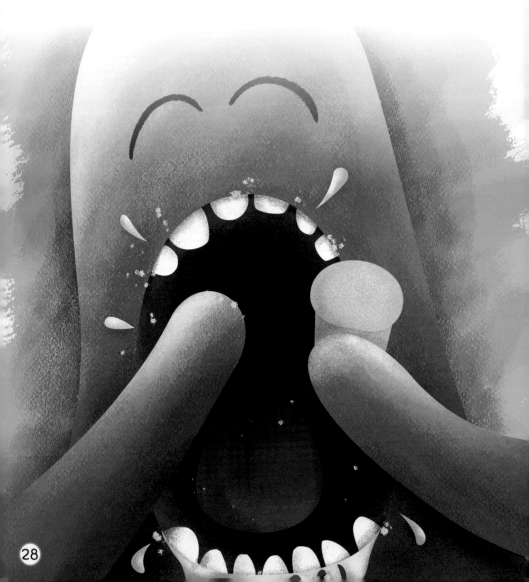

"As long as you are smiling, then we can smile!" said Zozo with a big grin.

The Monster Cook Book

1. What does The Monster Cook Book look like?

2. What did the monsters from the Moon cook for the monsters on Earth with three eyes?
   (a) Chips that crunch
   (b) Fish smoothies that smell
   (c) Green sausages

3. How did the monsters from the Moon travel to Earth?

4. Do you think the monsters from the Moon were glad that all the food they made was eaten?

5. If you were cooking for the monsters from the Moon, what food would you make for them?

©This edition published 2021.
First published in 2020.
BookLife Publishing Ltd.
King's Lynn, Norfolk PE30 4LS

ISBN 978-1-83927-305-6

The Monster Cook Book
Written by Shalini Vallepur
Illustrated by Drue Rintoul

An Introduction to BookLife Readers...

Our Readers have been specifically created in line with the London Institute of Education's approach to book banding and are phonetically decodable and ordered to support each phase of the Letters and Sounds document.

Each book has been created to provide the best possible reading and learning experience. Our aim is to share our love of books with children, providing both emerging readers and prolific page–turners with beautiful books that are guaranteed to provoke interest and learning, regardless of ability.

BOOK BAND GRADED using the Institute of Education's approach to levelling.

PHONETICALLY DECODABLE supporting each phase of Letters and Sounds.

EXERCISES AND QUESTIONS to offer reinforcement and to ascertain comprehension.

BEAUTIFULLY ILLUSTRATED to inspire and provoke engagement, providing a variety of styles for the reader to enjoy whilst reading through the series.

AUTHOR INSIGHT:
SHALINI VALLEPUR

Passionate about books from a very young age, Shalini Vallepur received the award of Norfolk County Scholar for her outstanding grades. Later on she read English at the University of Leicester, where she stayed to complete her Modern Literature MA. Whilst at university, Shalini volunteered as a Storyteller to help children learn to read, which gave her experience and expertise in the way children pick up and retain information. She used her knowledge and her background and implemented them in the 32 books that she has written for BookLife Publishing. Shalini's writing easily takes us to different worlds, and the serenity and quality of her words are sure to captivate any child who picks up her books.

PHASE 5

/ou/
ea/i_e/

This book focuses on the phonemes /ou/ /ea/ and /i_e/ and is an orange level 6 book band.